AN IMPRINT OF

SCHOLASTIC

NEW YORK TORONTO LONDON AUCKLAND SYDNEY MEXICO CITY NEW DELHI HONG KONG BUENOS AIRES

The Goosebumps book series created by Parachute Press, Inc.

Library of Congress Cataloging-in-Publication Data is available.

ISBN 0-439-84124-0 (hardcover) / ISBN 0-439-84125-9 (paperback)

12 11 10 9 8 7 6 5 4 3 2 1   06 07 08 09 10

First edition, September 2006

Edited by Sheila Keenan

Book design by Richard Amari

Creative Director: David Saylor

Printed in the United States of America   23

ADAPTED AND ILLUSTRATED BY

Gabriel Hernandez

IT ALL BEGAN WHEN WE MOVED TO FLORIDA.
I CAN STILL HEAR MY DAD TELLING US THIS WAS THE CHANCE OF A LIFETIME, AN ADVENTURE WE'D NEVER FORGET.
HE COULDN'T HAVE KNOWN BACK THEN HOW RIGHT HE WAS!

HEY, EMILY! LOOK AT THAT!
OUR NEW HOUSE WAS AT THE EDGE OF THE SWAMP. I COULDN'T WAIT TO EXPLORE. I STOOD IN THE BACKYARD WITH THE BINOCULARS MY DAD HAD GIVEN ME FOR MY BIRTHDAY AND GAZED TOWARD THE SWAMP.
IT'S A CRANE.
LET'S FOLLOW IT.

NO WAY. IT'S TOO HOT.
MEET MY SISTER EMILY. SHE CRIED FOR DAYS WHEN WE MOVED HERE FROM VERMONT. SHE DIDN'T WANT TO MISS HER SENIOR YEAR IN HIGH SCHOOL.
EMILY, TAKE A SHORT WALK WITH GRADY. YOU'RE NOT DOING ANYTHING ELSE.
BUT, MOM-
GO AHEAD, EM.
DAD AND MOM ARE BOTH SCIENTISTS. THEY WORK TOGETHER ON A LOT OF PROJECTS.
THEY GOT SIX SWAMP DEER FROM SOUTH AMERICA. THEY WANT TO SEE IF THESE DEER CAN SURVIVE IN THE SWAMPS IN FLORIDA. SO HERE WE ARE, LIVING IN FLORIDA WITH SIX WEIRD-LOOKING DEER IN OUR BACKYARD.
COME ON, EMILY. JUST A SHORT WALK. VERY SHORT.
NO.
IT WILL BE INTERESTING, MORE INTERESTING THAN STANDING AROUND IN THE HEAT ARGUING WITH YOUR BROTHER
WELL ...
GREAT! LET'S GO!

YUCK. GNATS. I HATE GNATS. IT MAKES ME ITCHY JUST TO LOOK AT THEM.
HEY- WHAT WAS THAT?
AN ALLIGATOR! A HUNGRY ALLIGATOR!
WHAT'S YOUR PROBLEM, EM? IT WAS JUST SOME KIND OF LIZARD.
YOU'RE A CREEP, GRADY.
HA, HA, HA!
IT'S TOO ITCHY IN THIS SWAMP. LET'S HEAD BACK.
JUST A LITTLE BIT FARTHER.
HEY- ANOTHER POND!

IT'S QUICKSAND!
WHOAAAA!!!
GOTCHA!
NOT FUNNY!
IT ISN'T QUICKSAND, DORK. IT'S A PEAT BOG.
WHAT'S A PEAT BOG?
THE POND IS THICK BECAUSE IT HAS PEAT MOSS GROWING IN IT. THE MOSS ABSORBS 25 TIMES ITS OWN WEIGHT IN WATER.
IT'S GROSS-LOOKING.
DRINK SOME, SEE HOW IT TASTES.
I'M NOT THIRSTY.
BLORP
LET'S GET GOING. I'M REALLY HOT.

THIS WAY.
ARE YOU SURE? I DON'T THINK WE'VE BEEN HERE BEFORE.
WE BOTH REALIZED WE WERE LOST. COMPLETELY **LOST.**
HEY, LOOK...
DO YOU THINK SOMEONE LIVES HERE? IN THE MIDDLE OF THE SWAMP?
MAYBE HE CAN TELL US WHICH WAY TO GET HOME.
MAYBE.
A...ANYONE HOME?

IT'S A HIDEOUT. A CRIMINAL. A BANK ROBBER. OR A KILLER.
HE'S HIDING HERE.
SHHH!!!!
ANYONE HOME?
ANYONE HOME?
ANYONE IN THERE?
CCCRREEEAAAKKKK

AAAAA
AAAAA
AAAAAAAAAAAAAAA
AAAAAAAAAAA
EMILY! WAIT UP! HE'S CHASING US!
RUN, GRADY, RUN!
HEY, THIS LOOKS FAMILIAR. LET'S GO!

HE-HE'S GONE! WE LOST HIM!
WELCOME BACK, EXPLORERS
HOME, SWEET HOME!
WE THOUGHT YOU GOT LOST.
WE DID!
YOU WHAT?
WE GOT LOST AND THEN A MAN CHASED US!
A STRANGE MAN WITH LONG, WHITE HAIR. HE LIVES IN A HUT IN THE MIDDLE OF THE SWAMP!
THE SWAMP HERMIT.
WHO?
THE GUY IN THE HARDWARE STORE TOLD ME ABOUT HIM. HE SAID HE WAS STRANGE, BUT PERFECTLY HARMLESS. BEEN LIVING IN THE SWAMP BY HIMSELF MOST OF HIS LIFE. NO ONE EVEN KNOWS HIS NAME.
MAYBE THEY SHOULDN'T GO BACK IN THE SWAMP BY THEMSELVES.
WELL, I TOLD YOU THIS WAS GOING TO BE AN ADVENTURE.
DON'T WORRY. YOU WON'T CATCH ME BACK IN THAT SWAMP.
COME WITH ME, GRADY. TIME TO FEED THE DEER.

THAT NIGT AFTER DINNER, I FELT A LITTLE HOMESICK. I THOUGHT ABOUT MY FRIENDS BACK IN VERMONT AND HOW WE USED TO HANG OUT.
I DECIDED TO TAKE A WALK.
HEY!
THE SWAMP HERMIT!!!
I SAW YOU FROM MY YARD. I LIVE OVER THERE. YOU JUST MOVED IN?
YEAH. I'M GRADY TUCKER. WHAT'S YOUR NAME?
WILL. **WILL BLAKE**.
WILL SAID HE WAS MY AGE, BUT HE LOOKED LIKE A FOOTBALL LINEMAN.
HOW LONG HAVE YOU LIVED HERE?
A FEW MONTHS.
ARE THERE ANY OTHER KIDS OUR AGE AROUND?
YEAH. ONE.
BUT SHE'S A GIRL AND SHE'S KIND OF WEIRD.
HAVE YOU BEEN IN THE SWAMP?
YEAH. THIS AFTERNOON. MY SISTER AND I GOT LOST.
DO YOU KNOW WHY IT'S CALLED **FEVER SWAMP**?

YEAH. MY DAD TOLD ME THE STORY. I THINK IT WAS A HUNDRED YEARS AGO. EVERYONE IN TOWN CAME DOWN WITH A STRANGE FEVER.
LOTS OF PEOPLE DIED FROM IT. AND THOSE WHO DIDN'T, BEGAN ACTING VERY STRANGE: TALKING CRAZY, FALLING DOWN OR WALKING AROUND IN CIRCLES.
WEIRD.
EVER SINCE THAT TIME, THEY CALLED IT FEVER SWAMP.
I'VE GOT TO GO. HEY! MAYBE YOU AND I CAN GO EXPLORING IN THE SWAMP TOGETHER.
GREAT!
A FEW NIGHTS LATER, I HEARD THE HOWLS FOR THE FIRST TIME.
AAAAOOOOUL
AAAAOOOOUL
RIGHT OUTSIDE THE WINDOW. LONG, ANGRY HOWLS.

GRADY!
GRADY, IT'S ME, EMILY.
DID YOU HEAR THE HOWLS?
YES, THEY WOKE ME UP. LET'S TAKE A LOOK.
WHAT'S THAT?
SCRATCH SCRATCH
SCRATCH SCRATCH SCRATCH
DO YOU THINK ONE OF THE DEER ESCAPED?
DO YOU REALLY THINK A DEER WOULD SCRATCH AT THE DOOR?
WHAT'S GOING ON HERE?

IT'S PAST MIDNIGHT.
WE HEARD NOISES. HOWLS OUTSIDE.
AND THEN SOMETHING WAS SCRATCHING AT THE DOOR.
MAYBE IT WAS THE WIND.
LET'S CHECK THE DEER.
CLICK
YOU SEE? NOTHING.
IT'S HARD TO SLEEP IN A NEW HOUSE. THE SOUNDS ARE ALL SO NEW. BUT YOU'LL GET USED TO THEM.
NO MORE WANDERING AROUND TONIGHT, OKAY?
THE NEXT MORNING WAS SO BEAUTIFUL, I WONDERED IF THE HOWLS WERE JUST PART OF A DREAM.
AKES
G
WHERE ARE YOU GOING SO EARLY?
I WANT TO SEE IF WILL IS HOME, MOM. MAYBE WE'LL HANG OUT OR SOMETHING.

WHoOAAAAA!!
HELP! HELP! IT'S GOT ME! IT'S...
...LICKING MY FACE?
WHERE'D YOU COME FROM?
HE'S ENORMOUS. HE MUST WEIGH MORE THAN A HUNDRED POUNDS.
HE LIKES YOU.
BUT HE PRACTICALLY KILLED ME. HE SCARED ME TO DEATH, DIDN'T YOU, FELLA?
I WONDER WHO HE BELONGS TO. GRADY, CHECK HIS COLLAR.
NOTHING THERE.
MAYBE HE'S A STRAY. MAYBE THAT'S WHY HE WAS SCRATCHING AT THE DOOR LAST NIGHT.

HI!
HI, WILL. LOOK WHAT WE FOUND.
HAVE YOU SEEN THIS DOG BEFORE? DOES HE BELONG TO SOMEONE IN THE NEIGHBORHOOD?
NOPE. NEVER SEEN HIM.
HE LOOKS MORE LIKE A WOLF THAN A DOG.
YEAH. HE REALLY DOES.
LET'S CALL HIM WOLF. SEE? HE LIKES THE NAME! CAN I KEEP HIM?
WE'LL SEE.
THAT NIGHT MY PARENTS AGREED TO LET WOLF SLEEP IN MY ROOM.
I DON'T KNOW HOW LONG I SLEPT BEFORE I WAS AWAKENED BY A SUDDEN
CRASH

CRASH
CLING
BUMP
WOLF! STOP!
BUMP
HE'S TRYING TO GET OUTSIDE!
OPEN THE FRONT DOOR! LET HIM OUT BEFORE HE WRECKS THE HOUSE!
WHAT A MESS HE'S MADE!
HE'S HEADING TO THE SWAMP.
WOLF WILL HAVE TO STAY OUTSIDE.
BUT, DAD...
HE'S TOO BIG AND RESTLESS TO STAY IN THE HOUSE.
NOW MAYBE WE CAN ALL SLEEP IN PEACE.
WRONG.

BECAUSE A SHORT WHILE LATER...
AAAAAOOOUUUUOO
GRRRRRR
GROOAAR
GRRRRAAAR
WOLF???

AAAAOOOUUUUUUU
AFTER BREAKFAST THE NEXT MORNING, I LED DAD OUT TO THE BACKYARD. WHEN I SAW WHAT WAS LYING IN A HEAP ON THE GRASS, I STARTED TO GAG.
IT WAS A RABBIT THAT HAD BEEN RIPPED OPEN, NEARLY TORN IN HALF.
I'M GLAD THE DEER ARE SAFE INSIDE THAT PEN.
WOLF!
WOOF!
WOOF!
WOOF!
WOLF, DOWN! HA, HA HA!
YOUR DOG IS A KILLER.

WHAT?
LOOK WHAT HE DID TO THAT POOR BUNNY RABBIT.
WHOA! HOLD ON. WHO SAID WOLF DID **THIS**?
WHO ELSE COULD HAVE DONE IT? HE'S A KILLER.
NO WAY! YOU HAVE NO PROOF!
GRADY, WOLF MAY BE A BIT OF A HUNTER.
BUT, DAD. DIDN'T YOU HEAR THOSE **HOWLS** LAST NIGHT? DOGS DON'T HOWL LIKE THAT.
THEN WHAT WAS IT?
YES, I HEARD THEM. THEY SOUNDED MORE LIKE WOLF HOWLS, OR MAYBE A COYOTE. BUT I'D BE VERY SURPRISED TO FIND THEM IN THIS SWAMP AREA.
LET'S JUST BE CAREFUL AROUND WOLF. HE SEEMS GENTLE, BUT WE REALLY DON'T KNOW ANYTHING ABOUT HIM.
I'M GOING TO STAY AS FAR AWAY FROM THAT **MONSTER** AS I CAN.
DAD GOT A SHOVEL AND BOX TO CARRY AWAY THE DEAD RABBIT IN.

YOU AREN'T A MONSTER, ARE YOU, BOY?
THAT WASN'T YOU I SAW LAST NIGHT, WAS IT?
WOLF SEEMED TO BE TRYING TO TELL ME SOMETHING. BUT I HAD NO IDEA WHAT IT COULD BE.
THAT NIGHT I DIDN'T HEAR THE HOWLS.
I WOKE UP IN THE MIDDLE OF THE NIGHT AND STARED OUT THE WINDOW. WOLF WAS GONE, PROBABLY EXPLORING THE SWAMP.
IN THE MORNING, I KNEW HE'D COME RUNNING BACK TO GREET ME.
HEY, WHAT'S UP?
HI, WILL.
WANT TO GO EXPLORING? YOU KNOW. IN THE SWAMP?
YEAH. SURE.
MOM, I'M GOING TO THE SWAMP WITH WILL.
BE CAREFUL, GRADY.

DID YOU HEAR ABOUT MR. WARNER? HE LIVES WITH HIS WIFE IN THE VERY LAST HOUSE ON THE BLOCK.
WHAT ABOUT HIM?
HE'S MISSING. HE DIDN'T COME HOME LAST NIGHT.
FROM WHERE?
FROM THE SWAMP. MRS. WARNER SAID HE WENT HUNTING WILD TURKEYS IN THE SWAMP YESTERDAY AFTERNOON... AND HE HASN'T COME BACK.
MAYBE HE GOT LOST.
NO WAY. NOT MR. WARNER. HE'S LIVED HERE A LONG TIME. HE WOULDN'T GOT LOST.
THEN MAYBE THE WEREWOLF GOT HIM!
CASSIE O'ROURKE! WHAT ARE YOU DOING HERE?
FOLLOWING YOU.

YOU ARE THE NEW KID. GRADY, RIGHT?
HI.
WHAT DID YOU SAY ABOUT A WEREWOLF?
DON'T START WITH THAT STUFF AGAIN. IT'S STUPID.
THERE'S A WEREWOLF IN THE SWAMP!
AND I'M GOING TO FLAP MY WINGS AND FLY TO MARS.
YOU'RE JUST AFRAID, WILL BLAKE!
YOU'VE GOT A GOOD IMAGINATION, CASSIE. I GUESS YOU WATCH A LOT OF SCARY MOVIES.
DO YOU HEAR THE HOWLING SOUNDS AT NIGHT?
YEAH.
THOSE HOWLS AREN'T HUMAN! THEY COME FROM A WEREWOLF THAT HAS JUST KILLED!
OOOH! STOP! YOU'RE MAKING ME SHAKE ALL OVER.
THERE'S NO SUCH THING AS WEREWOLVES... UNLESS MAYBE YOU'RE ONE!
VERY FUNNY.
WHAT DOES THE WEREWOLF LOOK LIKE? DOES IT HAVE RED HAIR AND FRECKLES?
TH-THERE'S THE WEREWOLF!!

THE SWAMP HERMIT!
IT'S HIM! IT'S THE WEREWOLF!
CASSIE, SHUT UP! HE'LL HEAR YOU!
HE SEES US!
RUN! COME ON! RUN!!!

I'M THE WEREWOLF!!
AAAAAA AAA AAA AAA
AAAAAAA
HA HA HA! I'M THE WEREWOLF!!
THUMP
UNGH!

HELP! WILL! CASSIE!
GO ON. GO. JUST TEASING YOU.
W-WHAT?
GO. I'M NOT GOING TO BITE YOU.
YIP!

THIS DOG YOURS?
YEAH. I...FOUND HIM.
WATCH OUT FOR HIM.
W-WATCH OUT FOR HIM?
WHAT DO YOU MEAN?
WOOF!
WOLF- WHY DIDN'T YOU PROTECT ME?
ARE YOU A BIG COWARD? YOU SOUND REAL TOUGH, BUT YOU'RE ACTUALLY A BIG CHICKEN? IS THAT YOUR PROBLEM?

WHAT HAPPENED? WHAT HAPPENED TO GRADY?
HE WAS BITTEN BY A WEREWOLF!
I'M OKAY. I THINK I WAS MAINLY SCARED. LET'S GO HOME.
CASSIE HAS WEREWOLVES ON THE BRAIN. SHE THINKS THE SWAMP HERMIT IS A WEREWOLF.
THAT OLD SWAMP HERMIT IS SUPPOSED TO BE HARMLESS.
WELL, HE GAVE US A REAL SCARE. HE CHASED US THROUGH THE SWAMP, YELLING "I'M THE WEREWOLF!"
YOU SHOULD STAY AWAY FROM HIM.
DO YOU BELIEVE IN WEREWOLVES?
YOUR MOM AND I ARE SCIENTISTS. WE'RE NOT SUPPOSED TO BELIEVE IN SUPERNATURAL THINGS LIKE WEREWOLVES.
YOUR FATHER IS A WEREWOLF. I HAVE TO SHAVE HIS BACK EVERY MORNING SO HE'LL LOOK HUMAN.
I'M SERIOUS. HAVEN'T YOU HEARD THE WEIRD SOUNDS AT NIGHT?
THE HOWLS DIDN'T START UNTIL THAT DOG SHOWED UP. YOUR DOG IS A WEREWOLF!
GIVE ME A BREAK!
ENOUGH WEREWOLF TALK!

THE MOON WILL LOOK FULL FOR ONLY TWO MORE NIGHTS.
IF THE HOWLS STOP AFTER TOMORROW NIGHT, WE'LL KNOW IT WAS A WEREWOLF, HOWLING AT THE FULL MOON.
AAAOOOUUU
AAAOOUUU
AAOOUU

I'M AFRAID YOUR DOG IS A KILLER.

THE NEXT MORNING...
I'M GOING TO HAVE TO TAKE WOLF TO THE POUND.
BUT THEY'LL KILL HIM!
I KNOW HOW YOU FEEL, GRADY. BUT THE DOG IS A KILLER.
IT WASN'T WOLF! I HEARD THE HOWLS!
IT WAS A WEREWOLF, DAD! THERE'S A WEREWOLF IN THE SWAMP! CASSIE WAS RIGHT!
GRADY...
I KNOW I'M RIGHT, DAD! IT'S BEEN A FULL MOON. IT'S A WEREWOLF. THE SWAMP HERMIT! HE DID IT, DAD!!
GRADY, STOP NOW!
GO LOOK AT THE PAW PRINTS ON THE GROUND. I CAN'T TAKE ANY MORE CHANCES.
I HAVE NO CHOICE...

NO!
GRADY!!!
WHA...?!
RUN, WOLF, RUN!
HEY!
GO, BOY GO!

THAT WAS DUMB, GRADY.
WOLF WILL COME BACK LATER. WHEN HE DOES, I'LL HAVE TO TAKE HIM AWAY.
BUT, DAD-
NO MORE DISCUSSION.
COME HELP ME GET THE DEER PEN PATCHED UP.
ALL DAY LONG, I WATCHED THE SWAMP. I FELT NERVOUS, SHAKY.
BY EVENING, WOLF HADN'T RETURNED.
MY WHOLE FAMILY WAS TENSE. AT DINNER, WE HARDLY SPOKE.
I WENT TO BED EARLY. I WAS REALLY TIRED FROM BEING UP MOST OF THE NIGHT BEFORE.
IT WAS THE LAST NIGHT OF THE FULL MOON, BUT HEAVY BLANKETS OF CLOUDS COVERED THE MOONLIGHT.
I SETTLED MY HEAD INTO THE PILLOW AND TRIED TO SLEEP.
THEN THE HOWLS STARTED...

AAOOOUL
WOLF!
GRRRRRR
HE WAS PACING AND GROWLING, AS IF SOMETHING WAS REALLY TROUBLING HIM...
OR SCARING HIM!
I FUMBLED INTO MY SNEAKERS. I HAD TO FOLLOW WOLF.
I'M GOING TO PROVE ONCE AND FOR ALL HE ISN'T A KILLER OR A WEREWOLF.

CRACK
HEY! WHO'S THERE?
GRADY- IT'S YOU!
WILL- WHAT ARE YOU DOING OUT HERE?
I HEARD THE HOWLS. I DECIDED TO INVESTIGATE.
ME, TOO. I'M GLAD TO SEE YOU! WE CAN EXPLORE TOGETHER.
LOOK! THERE'S WOLF!

HE WENT THIS WAY! FOLLOW ME!
HEY, WILL?
WILL???

CRACKLE
WILL, IS THAT YOU? WHERE ARE YOU?
THE SWAMP HERMIT? OH, NO!
NO! NO!
NO!

GRRAOOORR
UNGH!
THUMP

YOU SHOULDN'T HAVE COME TO THE SWAMP AT NIGHT, GRADY ...
NOT WHEN THE MOON IS FULL!!
W...WILL?
AAAOOUUUUU
WILL! NO! WILL-!
AAAAAAAA
CHOMP

WOLF!
WOOF WOOF WOOF GRRRR
GRAAAH
WOLF! I KNEW IT WASN'T YOU. IT WAS WILL...
...ALL ALONG!

THAT WAS A MONTH AGO.
THE LAST THING I REMEMBER THEN IS SEEING **WILL** RUN AWAY ON ALL FOURS. **WOLF** FOLLOWED. I HEARD WILL UTTER A CRY OF PAIN, A WAIL OF DEFEAT.
I SANK DOWN INTO BLUE-BLACK DARKNESS . . .
. . . AND WOKE UP IN MY OWN BEDROOM.

HOW- HOW DID I GET HERE?

MOM AND DAD SAID THE SWAMP HERMIT FOUND ME IN THE SWAMP AND CARRIED ME HOME.

HE TOLD THEM HE SAW WOLF CHASE SOME KIND OF ANIMAL AWAY FROM ME.

I TOLD MY PARENTS THE WHOLE STORY. THEY DIDN'T BELIEVE ME, OF COURSE.
DAD WENT RIGHT OVER TO WILL'S HOUSE TO CHECK IT OUT.

THE HOUSE WAS DESERTED. IT LOOKED LIKE NO ONE HAD LIVED THERE FOR MONTHS.

WILL WAS GONE.
BUT I KNOW I'LL NEVER FORGET HIM. HE CHANGED MY LIFE.
I'M STANDING AT MY BEDROOM WINDOW NOW, WATCHING THE FULL MOON RISING THROUGH THE TREES.
CASSIE WAS RIGHT. WHEN A WEREWOLF BITES YOU, HE PASSES ON THE CURSE.
AAAOOOUUUU
THERE'S WOLF WAITING FOR ME, EAGER TO DO SOME NIGHT EXPLORING IN THE SWAMP.
MY SWAMP. WITH WILL OUT OF THE WAY, THE SWAMP IS MINE, ALL MINE!

NOW, I'M THE WEREWOLF OF FEVER SWAMP.
AND I'M READY TO HUNT!

THE SCARECROW WALKS AT MIDNIGHT

ADAPTED AND ILLUSTRATED BY

Greg Ruth

HEY JODIE-
WAIT UP!
LOOK IN THE DICTIONARY FOR SLOWPOKE, AND YOU'LL SEE MARK'S PICTURE.
I LIKE THE DICTIONARY, JODIE...
...SOMETIMES I READ IT FOR HOURS.
STANLEY WAS THE HIRED HAND ON MY GRANDPARENT'S FARM.
HEY MARK,
GET A MOVE ON!
YOU LOOK NICE, JODIE.
HOW OLD ARE YOU NOW?
TWELVE...
...AND MARK IS ELEVEN.
THAT MAKES TWENTY-THREE!
YOU NEVER KNOW WHAT STANLEY'S GOING TO SAY.
MOM AND DAD SAID IT WAS MY RESPONSIBILITY TO MAKE SURE MARK GOT OUT AND ENJOYED THE FARM.
CARRY MY BACKPACK FOR ME.
NO WAY!
CARRY IT YOURSELF!
WE WERE SO COOPED UP IN THE CITY ALL YEAR. THAT'S WHY THEY SENT US TO VISIT GRANDPA CURTIS AND GRANDMA MIRIAM FOR A MONTH EACH SUMMER-
-TO ENJOY THE GREAT OUTDOORS.

MR. MORTIMER...
...DOESN'T FARM HIS PLACE ANYMORE.
WHY NOT?
HE DIED.
YOU SEE?
YOU NEVER KNOW WHAT STANLEY IS GOING TO SAY!

THE CORN IS SO HIGH ALREADY!
HAVE YOU EATEN ANY YET?
JUST AT DINNER.
THE SCARECROW WALKS AT MIDNIGHT...
HUH?
THE SCARECROW WALKS AT MIDNIGHT.
I READ IT IN THE BOOK.
I DIDN'T KNOW WHAT TO SAY, SO I JUST LAUGHED.

JODIE, WHERE'D YOU GET THAT BLOND HAIR? THERE AREN'T ANY BLONDS IN MY FAMILY.
I BET YOU GOT IT FROM A STORE.
YOU'RE RIGHT, GRANDPA. IT'S A WIG.
HEY GRANDPA-
DID YOU GET CABLE YET?
CABLE TV? NOT YET. BUT WE STILL GET THREE CHANNELS.
HOW MANY MORE DO WE NEED?
LET'S GO IN. I MADE SOUP AND SANDWICHES.
WE'LL HAVE CHICKEN AND CORN TONIGHT.
I KNOW HOW YOU TWO LOVE IT.

STANLEY WILL HAVE TO SHOW YOU HIS SCARECROWS.
WON'T YOU STANLEY?
I *MADE* THEM.
THE *BOOK*— IT TOLD ME HOW.
ECCHMM!
LET'S *CHANGE* THE SUBJECT.
SO...
STANLEY- WHERE'S STICKS?
WENT TO TOWN.
WENT TO TOWN, RIDING ON A PONY.
STANLEY LIVED WITH HIS TEENAGE SON, STICKS.
IF YOU KIDS ARE FINISHED, WHY NOT GO WITH STANLEY-
-HE'LL GIVE YOU A TOUR OF THE FARM.
YOU ALWAYS ENJOY THAT.

SO MANY SCARECROWS!
STANLEY, LAST SUMMER THERE WAS ONLY ONE.
WHY ARE THERE SO MANY NOW?
STANLEY DIDN'T REPLY. HE DIDN'T SEEM TO HEAR ME.
WE'VE SEEN THE FARM A *HUNDRED* TIMES. WHY DO WE HAVE TO TAKE THE GRAND TOUR *AGAIN*?
COOL YOUR JETS.
WE *ALWAYS* TAKE A TOUR OF THE FARM. IT'S *TRADITION*.
LET'S SEE IF THE CORN'S READY.
GROSS!

NO!!
THAT'S BAD LUCK!
THE BOOK SAYS SO. THAT'S VERY BAD LUCK!
IT'S OKAY, STANLEY.
THIS HAPPENS SOMETIMES.
GRANDPA TOLD ME. SOMETIMES WORMS GET INTO THE CORN.
NO. IT'S BAD.
THE BOOK- IT SAYS SO.
WHAT BOOK?
MY BOOK. MY SUPERSTITION BOOK.
UH-OH. STANLEY SHOULDN'T HAVE A BOOK ABOUT SUPER-STITIONS....
HE WAS ALREADY THE MOST SUPERSTITIOUS PERSON IN THE WORLD!
IT'S A GOOD BOOK- IT'S TRUE! IT'S ALL TRUE!

STANLEY'S ALWAYS BEEN STRANGE, BUT I'VE NEVER SEEN HIM GET SO UPSET ABOUT SOMETHING AS UNIMPORTANT AS A BAD EAR OF CORN.
SHOW US THE SCARECROWS.
YEAH, LET'S SEE THEM.
OKAY. THE SCARECROWS.
YOU MADE THESE?
I MADE THEM.
THE BOOK SHOWED ME HOW.
THEY'RE PRETTY SCARY LOOKING.

I MADE THEM WALK, JODIE.
THE BOOK TOLD ME HOW.
HUH?
I MADE THEM WALK LAST WEEK AND NOW I'M THE BOSS.
DO YOU MEAN—
IT'S ALIVE!!
STICKS! YOU CREEP!
HA HA HA
YOU CITY KIDS SURE SCARE EASY.
HA HA
YOU REALLY THOUGHT THE SCARE-CROW MOVED, DIDN'T YOU, JODIE?

I CAN MAKE THEM WALK. I DID IT.
IT'S ALL IN THE BOOK.
YEAH, SURE, DAD.
I DON'T THINK IT'S BEEN EASY FOR STICKS GROWING UP ON THE FARM. STANLEY IS MORE LIKE A KID THAN A FATHER.
THE CORN HAS EARS. THERE ARE SPIRITS IN THE FIELD....
THINGS ARE DIFFERENT HERE....
THE BOOK IS ALL TRUE.
HEY MARK, YOU'VE GOT SOMETHING ON YOUR BACK.
TURN AROUND.
AAAAAHH!
STICKS STUFFED A WORMY COB INTO MARK'S SHIRT.
YYAAAAAAAAAAHHHHHH!!!
STICKS WAS ALWAYS PLAYING STUPID JOKES ON US. BUT I STILL HAD TO LAUGH.

LATER THAT NIGHT...
MARK!
MARK- COME HERE!
HURRY!
JODIE, WHAT IS IT?
THE SCARECROWS.
THEY'RE MOVING.
WHAT'S YOUR PROBLEM JODIE? IT'S JUST THE WIND.
DON'T YOU SEE? THEY'RE ALL MOVING TOGETHER!
WE HAVE TO TELL GRANDPA KURT!
...
MAYBE WE'D BETTER WAIT TILL TOMORROW.
WE RUSHED DOWN-STAIRS BUT OUR GRANDPARENTS HAD GONE TO BED.

LAST NIGHT, MARK AND I WERE LOOKING OUT AT THE SCARECROWS....
THEY WERE MOVING!
IT WAS THE WIND.
YOU SURE?
YEAH.
IT WAS THE WIND.
IT WAS THE WIND.
BUT THEY WERE TRYING TO GET OFF THEIR POLES!
WE SAW THEM!
IT'S GOING TO BE A SUNNY DAY!
AFTER YOU TAKE THE COWS OUT TO PASTURE, MAYBE YOU, MARK, AND STANLEY COULD GO FISHING.
YEP!
LOOKS LIKE A REAL PRETTY DAY!
BUT...
MY GRANDPARENTS HAD CHANGED. THEY BOTH SEEMED TENSE. UNCOMFORTABLE.

HEY, WAIT UP STANLEY!
CRACK!
STANLEY- WAIT!
STICKS...
IS THAT YOU?
STICKS?

NO!!
JODIE! WHAT'S THE MATTER?
I SAW IT!
I SAW A SCARECROW.
YOU DID? A SCARECROW? REALLY?
I COULD SEE HE WAS REALLY STARTING TO GET SCARED.
I...I DON'T THINK SO. I'M SORRY, STANLEY.
I DIDN'T WANT TO FRIGHTEN STANLEY.
WELL... MAYBE IT WAS THE SHADOWS...
THIS IS VERY BAD.
THIS IS VERY BAD.
I HAVE TO READ THE BOOK.
STANLEY STOP!
COME BACK! DON'T LEAVE US DOWN HERE!!
THIS IS VERY BAD.

STANLEY-
WAIT!
MY HEART POUNDED. UP AHEAD, I SAW STANLEY RUNNING INTO HIS LITTLE HOUSE.
WAIT!!
I DECIDED TO FIND GRANDPA KURT TO TELL HIM ABOUT THE SCARECROWS.
CRAK!
GRANDPA?
GRANDPA KURT?
ARE YOU IN THERE?

GRANDPA KURT?
ARE YOU-
HEY!
HEY! WHO'S THERE?
HEY, STOP!
HEY! LET ME OUT!
LET ME OUT OF HERE!!

SCRAPE
SCRAPE
WHO'S...
...WHO'S THERE?
SCRAPE
SCRAPE
SCRAPE
PLEASE...
...PLEASE DON'T.
SCRAPE
SCRAPE
SCRAPE
SCRAPE
SCRAPE
SCRAPE
SCRAPE
SCRAPE
GO AWAY!
SCRAPE

MY HEART WAS STILL POUNDING. I POKED MY HEAD OUT THE WINDOW AND GAZED TO THE GROUND....
AH!!
SCRAPE
SCRAPE
A SCARECROW!
IT JERKED ITS ARMS AND LEGS AT THE SOUND OF MY SCREAM.
SCRAPE
SCRAPE
AS I STARED IN DISBELIEF, IT SCURRIED AROUND THE SIDE OF THE BARN, HOBBLING ON ITS STRAW LEGS.
YES! THE HEAVY ROPE THAT MARK AND I USED TO SWING TO THE GROUND WAS STILL TIED TO THE SIDE!
I CAN ESCAPE!

I WANTED TO CATCH UP WITH THE SCARECROW, TO SEE IF-
HEY!
STICKS!
WHY DO YOU KEEP TRYING TO SCARE US?
HUH?
I'M NOT STUPID.
I KNOW YOU WERE THE SCARECROW JUST NOW!
SCARECROW? YOU'RE TOTALLY CRAZY!
YOU WERE DRESSED AS ONE, OR CARRIED ONE HERE AND PULLED IT WITH A STRING OR SOMETHING.
WHY DO YOU KEEP TRYING TO SCARE MARK AND ME?
YOU SCARED YOUR DAD TOO.
DAD?
YOU SAY HE WAS SCARED?
YOUR JOKE HAS GONE FAR ENOUGH.
JUST STOP IT!
I'VE GOT TO FIND DAD!
HE COULD DO SOMETHING TERRIBLE!

STICKS DIDN'T FIND HIS DAD UNTIL JUST BEFORE DINNER. THAT'S THE NEXT TIME I SAW HIM, TOO.
HE WAS HOLDING HIS BIG SUPERSTITION BOOK, TIGHTLY UNDER HIS ARM.
JODIE-
HE WHISPERED.
DON'T TELL YOUR GRANDPA ABOUT THE SCARECROW.
HUH?
DON'T TELL YOUR GRANDPA. IT WILL ONLY UPSET HIM.
WE DON'T WANT TO FRIGHTEN HIM, DO WE?
BUT, STANLEY-
DON'T TELL.
I'LL TAKE CARE OF THE SCARECROW.
I HAVE THE BOOK.

AFTER DINNER, GRANDPA ALWAYS LOVEDTO GAZE AT THE FIRE AND TELL SCARY STORIES.
BUT TONIGHT HE SHRUGGED WHEN I ASKED HIM FOR A STORY.
...
WISH I KNEW SOME GOOD STORIES.
BUT I'VE RUN CLEAN OUT.

WHAT'S HIS PROBLEM?
BEATS ME. EVERYONE HERE SEEMS SO... DIFFERENT.
EXCEPT FOR STICKS. HE'S STILL TRYING TO SCARE US CITY KIDS.
LET'S JUST IGNORE HIM.
LET'S JUST PRETEND WE DON'T SEE HIM RUNNING AROUND IN HIS STUPID SCARECROW COSTUME.
I AGREED. IGNORE THE SCARECROWS.
I'M NOT GOING TO THINK ABOUT SCARECROWS AGAIN.
I FOUND MYSELF THINKING ABOUT BY BEST FRIEND SHAWNA.
I WONDERED IF SHE WAS HAVING A GOOD TIME AT CAMP.
I THOUGHT ABOUT SOME OF MY OTHER FRIENDS.
MOST OF THEM WERE JUST HANGING AROUND THIS SUMMER, NOT DOING MUCH OF-

HUH?
SCRAPE
WHO'S... WHO'S THERE?
GRANDPA KURT!
GRANDPA KURT- WHAT ARE YOU DOING HERE? WHY-
SCRAPE
SCRAPE
NO!!

WHAT'S-
GRANDPA-
PLEASE NO!!
GRANDPA
WHAT'S WRONG?
WHAT'S
HAPPENING?!
NOOO!!!
OH
HELP!!
PLEASE
HELP!!

GRANDMA MIRIAM HELP!!
WHAT'S HAPPENING?
OH!
...HELP.
IT'S GOING TO BE A SUNNY DAY!
NO!!!
A DREAM.
...IT HAD ALL BEEN A FRIGHTENING NIGHTMARE.

THE NEXT MORNING I WAS TEMPTED TO TELL GRANDMA ABOUT MY SCARY NIGHTMARE, BUT HER EYES REMAINED DULL.
NO PANCAKES?
I'VE... FORGOTTEN HOW TO MAKE THEM.
CORN FLAKES
ARE YOU OKAY, GRANDMA? IS EVERYTHING OKAY HERE?
GO HAVE YOUR RIDE. DON'T WORRY ABOUT ME.
BUMPING ALONG THESE TWO OLD NAGS WAS JUST OUR SPEED.
I WONDER IF THESE HORSES CAN STILL GET UP TO A TROT.
LET'S GIVE IT A TRY!
ALL RIGHT! COOL!
WHOOOA!!

IT ALL HAPPENED SO FAST.
OHHHH..
MARK?
MY WRIST...
...I THINK I BROKE IT.
YOU FELL TOO?

JODIE...
STANLEY- IT'S YOU!
...ARE YOU ALL RIGHT?
WHAT A BAD FALL.
I WAS IN THE FIELD. AND I SAW IT.
I SAW THE SCARECROW....
...I SAW IT JUMP OUT.
WHERE'S MY HORSE?
SHE GALLOPED BACK TO THE BARN. FASTER THAN I'VE SEEN HER GO IN YEARS!

MY WRIST...
LOOK- IT'S STARTING TO SWELL UP....
OOOH, THAT'S BAD.
THAT'S BAD.
WE'D BETTER GET YOU BACK TO THE HOUSE AND PUT ICE ON IT.
CAN YOU GET BACK UP ON MAGGIE? I'LL RIDE BEHIND YOU.
I'M OKAY. TAKE MARK BACK ON THE HORSE.
I'LL WALK BACK.
IT'S JUST A SCARECROW. JUST A SCARECROW THAT STICKS TOSSED ONTO THE PATH.
MARK AND I COULD HAVE BEEN KILLED.
BUT WHY WAS STICKS TRYING TO HURT US?

I CAN'T DO THIS!
MY WRIST HURTS AGAIN. I CAN'T USE IT.
NO PROBLEM. YOU WON'T HAVE TO USE IT.
THINK THIS IS GOING TO WORK?
THINK WE'RE REALLY GOING TO SCARE STICKS?
I THINK SO.
I COULDN'T WAIT TO PAY STICKS BACK FOR TRYING TO FRIGHTEN US ALL WEEK.
I THINK STICKS IS IN FOR A TERRIFYING SURPRISE.
PUT YOUR ARMS UP STRAIGHT OUT AND DON'T MOVE A MUSCLE.
WHEN YOU HEAR ME BRING STICKS OVER, START TO STAGGER.
JUST KEEP THINKING HOW GREAT IT'LL BE WHEN STICKS SEES YOU AND THINKS YOU'RE A SCARECROW COME TO LIFE.

I WAS BREATHING HARD BY THE TIME I REACHED STANLEY'S HOUSE.
HOW WAS I GOING TO GET STICKS TO COME OUT ALONE WITHOUT HIS FATHER?
I DIDN'T WANT TO FRIGHTEN STANLEY....
MARK?
MARK GET BACK IN THE FIELD!
YOU'RE GOING TO RUIN EVERYTHING!
STICKS, IS THAT YOU?
WHAT ON EARTH?
IT REALLY IS A SCARECROW? BUT IT WALKED!
I WARNED YOU!
DAD USED HIS BOOK. HE CHANTED SOME WORDS AND THE SCARECROWS CAME TO LIFE!

WE WERE ALL SO FRIGHTENED. ESPECIALLY YOUR GRANDPARENTS.
THEY BEGGED DAD TO PUT THEM BACK TO SLEEP.
DID HE?
YES.
BUT FIRST THEY HAD TO PROMISE NOT TO LAUGH AT HIM ANYMORE.
THEY HAD TO DO WHATEVER DAD WANTED, BUT...
BUT WHAT?
SOME OF THE SCARECROWS ARE STILL ALIVE.
SOME OF THEM NEVER WENT BACK TO SLEEP.
N-NO!!
IT WALKS! THE SCARECROW WALKS!
NO DAD!
IT DIDN'T WALK! I DROPPED IT HERE!
IT DIDN'T WALK!
NO! IT WALKS!

WHERE'VE YOU BEEN?
DID WE BLOW IT? IS THE JOKE OVER? WHAT'S HAPPENING?
NO!
THE SCARECROWS WALK! I MUST TAKE CHARGE!
DAD, PLEASE!
WHAT'S GOING ON, JODIE?
NOT NOW MARK!
WE'VE GOT TO STOP MY DAD!
RUN!
GO WARN YOUR GRAND-PARENTS!
WHAT'S HAPPENING?

HEY!
GRANDPA KURT AND GRANDMA MIRIAM MUST HAVE HEARD OUR SHOUTS FROM THE CORNFIELD. THEY WERE WAITING FOR US.
DID YOU GET STANLEY UPSET?
IT WAS AN ACCIDENT! WE DIDN'T MEAN TO, REALLY!
MARK, WHY ARE YOU DRESSED LIKE THAT?
DID YOU DRESS LIKE THAT TO SCARE STANLEY?

NO! IT WAS SUPPOSED TO BE A JOKE!
JUST A JOKE!
WE WERE TRYING TO SCARE STICKS. BUT WHEN STANLEY SAW MARK...
THEY'RE ALIVE!
HELP US, PLEASE!
THEY WON'T OBEY ME!
THEY WON'T OBEY ME!

THEY MUST OBEY ME!
THE BOOK SAYS SO!
STANLEY! LISTEN TO ME! WHAT DOES THE BOOK SAY TO DO?
HOW DO YOU GET THEM UNDER CONTROL?
I DON'T KNOW!

SUPERSTITIONS
STOP!
I COMMAND YOU TO STOP!!
WHOA.
WHAT'S GOING ON HERE?
scratch
scratch
MARK! THEY'RE IMITATING YOU!
THEY THINK YOU'RE ONE OF THEM. THEY THINK YOU'RE THEIR LEADER.
BUT HOW DO I MAKE THEM GO BACK TO THEIR POLES?
HOW DO I MAKE THEM GO BACK TO BEING SCARECROWS?
PULL OFF YOUR SCARECROW HEAD.
BUT WHY?
IF YOU PULL OFF YOUR SCARECROW HEAD, THEN THEY'LL PULL OFF THEIRS, AND THEY'LL DIE.

I HELD MY BREATH. MY HEART WAS *POUNDING*.
NONE OF US MOVED. WE WERE WAITING FOR THE SCARECROWS TO FALL.
BUT THEY DIDN'T GO DOWN.
MARK, DO SOMETHING!
THEY'RE *NOT* FOLLOWING ME! I DON'T LOOK LIKE THEIR LEADER ANYMORE!

THE STRAW SMELLED SOUR.
DECAYED.
LET GO! LET GO!!
A STREAK OF ORANGE AGAINST THE DARKNESS.
STICKS!
I WAS SAVING THESE JUST IN CASE!
THE SCARECROWS LET GO OF US AND TRIED TO SCRAMBLE AWAY.
THE OLD COATS BURNED QUICKLY.
THE DRY STRAW BURST INTO FLAME.
IT'S OVER!
NEVER AGAIN.

THE HOUSE WAS QUIET THE NEXT AFTERNOON.
"I'VE LEARNED MY LESSON ABOUT THE SUPERSTITION BOOK," STANLEY SAID AT LUNCH.
"I'LL NEVER TRY TO BRING ANY SCARECROWS TO LIFE AGAIN. I WON'T EVEN *READ* THE PART ABOUT SCARECROWS!"
WE WERE ALL *GLAD* TO HEAR THAT.
IT FELT GOOD TO BE ALL ALONE TO THINK ABOUT WHAT HAD HAPPENED.
ALL ALONE...
THE ONLY ONE IN THE ROOM...
THE ONLY-
STANLEY?
WHAT CHAPTER HAVE YOU BEEN READING?

THE ABOMINABLE SNOWMAN OF PASADENA

ADAPTED AND ILLUSTRATED BY

Scott Morse

ALL MY LIFE, I'VE WANTED TO SEE SNOW.
I'M LUIS GARCIA AND I LIVE IN PASADENA, CALIFORNIA. MY WHOLE LIFE HAS BEEN SUN, SAND, AND CHLORINE. I'D NEVER FELT COLD, EVER...
UNTIL THE ADVENTURE...
PAY ATTENTION, KIDS. THIS IS GOING TO BE COOL.
DAD TAKES NATURE PHOTOS. HE JUST RETURNED FROM THE ROCKY MOUNTAINS.
I WISH YOU KIDS HAD SEEN THOSE BEARS... A WHOLE FAMILY OF THEM!
YOU SHOULD HAVE TAKEN US WITH YOU, DAD.
IT'S VERY COLD IN WYOMING THIS TIME OF THE YEAR.
HOW DO YOU KNOW, BRAINIAC?
I READ UP ON IT WHILE DAD WAS AWAY.
ANA GARCIA, MY SISTER. MISS KNOW-IT-ALL-- DRIVES ME CRAZY!

DID IT SNOW IN THE MOUNTAINS WHILE YOU WERE THERE, DAD?
SURE IT SNOWED.
DID YOU GO SKIING?
I WAS TOO BUSY WORKING.
IF THESE SHOTS COME OUT WELL, I CAN PUBLISH THEM IN A BOOK.
THAT'S WEIRD.
DAD, I HATE TO BREAK IT TO YOU, BUT THAT LOOKS LIKE A TEDDY BEAR.
THERE MUST BE SOME MISTAKE...WAIT TILL THE REST OF THE PHOTOS DEVELOP. YOU'LL SEE... THEY'RE AMAZING!
HUH?!
MORE TEDDY BEARS??!!!
DID I LOSE THE FILM ON THE PLANE SOMEHOW? SWITCH BAGS WITH SOMEONE? WHAT'S GOING ON?

LUIS! YOU'RE LAUGHING!
HEE HEE
HEE
HE
I CAN'T RESIST A PRACTICAL JOKE.
I BORROWED YOUR CAMERA BEFORE YOU LEFT AND SHOT MY OLD TEDDY BEAR, FOR A JOKE. THE REST OF THE FILM SHOULD HAVE YOUR REAL BEARS ON IT.
A JOKE?
I HAD NOTHING TO DO WITH IT, DAD.
LITTLE MISS GOODY-GOODY.
THEY DON'T LOOK AS DIFFERENT AS YOU'D THINK.
THIS ROLL CAME OUT GREAT, BUT I GOT A LOT MORE WORK TO DO HERE, KIDS. GO ON OUTSIDE FOR A WHILE, OKAY?
A WAVE OF HEAT BLASTED US WHEN WE OPENED THE DARKROOM DOOR.

WHAT DO YOU WANT TO DO?
I DON'T KNOW. IT'S SO *HOT!*
ANA? WHAT ARE YOU DOING?
I'M THINKING ABOUT THE SNOW IN DAD'S PICTURES. I THOUGHT IT WOULD MAKE ME FEEL COOLER.
IS IT WORKING?
NO...HOW CAN I IMAGINE SNOW IF I'VE NEVER *FELT* IT?
WE LIVE IN A SUBDIVISION IN THE SUBURBS.
IT'S SO BORING TO LOOK AT IT, IT MAKES ME FEEL EVEN HOTTER, SOMEHOW.

LET'S RIDE OUR BIKES. MAYBE THE BREEZE WILL COOL US OFF.
MAYBE LAUREN WILL WANT TO GO WITH US.

LAUREN SAX LIVES NEXT DOOR TO US.
IT'S *SO HOT!* THIS IS SUPPOSED TO BE WINTER! A NORMAL WINTER HAS SNOW AND ICE... WHAT DO WE GET? NOTHING BUT *SUN!*

KIDS! I HAVE GREAT NEWS... WILDERNESS MAGAZINE JUST CALLED. THEY WANT TO FLY ME TO ALASKA!
GREAT, DAD. YOU GET TO GO ON ANOTHER EXCITING TRIP WHILE WE STAY HERE AND DIE OF BOREDOM.
AND HEAT!
I GUESS YOU TWO WILL JUST HAVE TO COME ALONG WITH ME.
TO ALASKA?!
HURRAY!
YOU GUYS ARE SO LUCKY!
WE'LL GET TO SEE SNOW! TONS OF SNOW!
THEY WANT ME TO TRACK DOWN SOME KIND OF SNOW CREATURE--AN ABOMINABLE SNOWMAN! I'M SURE IT'S A WILD-GOOSE CHASE. BUT I'LL GET SOME GREAT SHOTS OF THE TUNDRA.
WHAT'S A TUNDRA?
I'LL HANDLE THIS ONE, DAD.
A TUNDRA IS A HUGE FROZEN PLAIN. IT EXISTS IN THE ARCTIC, IN ALASKA, AND IN RUSSIA. THE WORD TUNDRA COMES FROM THE RUSSIAN, MEANING...
ANY OTHER QUESTIONS, LAUREN?
THAT'S ALL I NEEDED TO KNOW.

I WATCHED FOR GIANT FOOTPRINTS AS WE FLEW. HOW BIG WOULD AN ABOMINABLE SNOWMAN'S FOOTSTEPS BE? BIG ENOUGH TO SEE FROM A LOW-FLYING PLANE?

CAN WE BUILD AN IGLOO AND SLEEP IN THAT?
WE'LL BE STAYING IN A LITTLE CABIN OUT IN THE TUNDRA.
YOU CAN'T JUST BUILD AN IGLOO, LUIS. IT'S NOT LIKE A SNOW FORT.

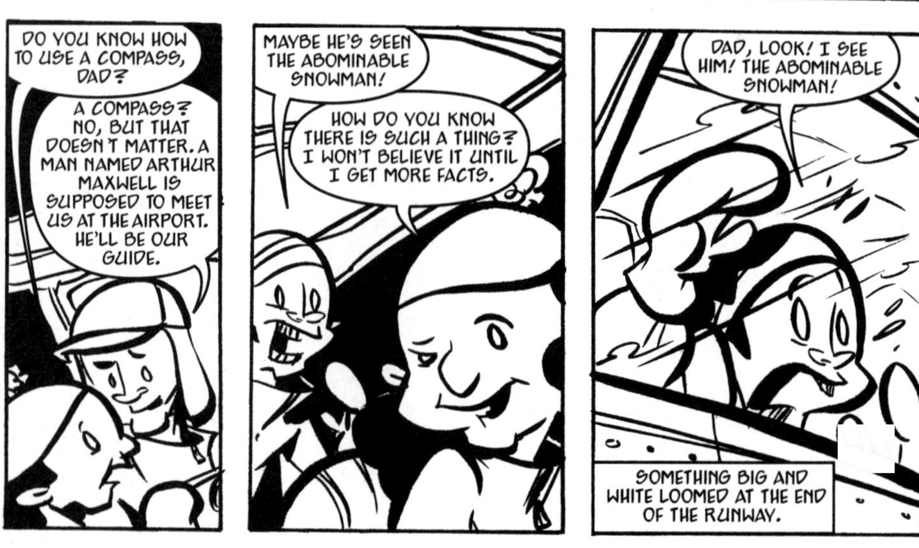
DO YOU KNOW HOW TO USE A COMPASS, DAD?
A COMPASS? NO, BUT THAT DOESN'T MATTER. A MAN NAMED ARTHUR MAXWELL IS SUPPOSED TO MEET US AT THE AIRPORT. HE'LL BE OUR GUIDE.
MAYBE HE'S SEEN THE ABOMINABLE SNOWMAN!
HOW DO YOU KNOW THERE IS SUCH A THING? I WON'T BELIEVE IT UNTIL I GET MORE FACTS.
DAD, LOOK! I SEE HIM! THE ABOMINABLE SNOWMAN!
SOMETHING BIG AND WHITE LOOMED AT THE END OF THE RUNWAY.

THE PLANE SQUEALED TO A STOP RIGHT IN FRONT OF THE BIG MONSTER.
THE POLAR BEAR IS A SYMBOL OF THE TOWN.
WELCOME TO IKNEK
LUIS KNEW THAT, HE WAS JUST PLAYING ONE OF HIS PRACTICAL JOKES.
UH, YEAH! I KNEW IT WAS A STATUE ALL ALONG.
YOU DID NOT, LUIS. YOU WERE REALLY SCARED!
ISN'T IT GREAT THE WAY THESE TWO KID EACH OTHER?
MR. GARCIA? I'M ARTHUR MAXWELL. NEED SOME HELP THERE?
HI! NICE TO MEET YOU.
YOU DIDN'T MENTION KIDS.

HOW FAR IS IT TO TOWN, ARTHUR?
HOW FAR? YOU'RE LOOKING AT IT.
IT'S NOT PASADENA, BUT WE CALL IT HOME THE DOGS CAN PULL YOUR SUPPLIES. WE'LL WALK BESIDE THE SLED.
WHY DO WE HAVE TO WALK?! WHY CAN'T WE TAKE A HELICOPTER OR SOMETHING?
BECAUSE I WANT TO TAKE PHOTOS ALONG THE WAY, LUIS. YOU NEVER KNOW WHAT YOU'LL COME ACROSS.
HAVE YOU EVER SEEN THIS SNOW CREATURE WE'RE LOOKING FOR?
CLICK
NEVER SEEN IT. HEARD ABOUT IT. LOTS OF STORIES.
WHAT KIND OF STORIES?
A COUPLE OF PEOPLE IN TOWN HAVE SEEN THE MONSTER.
WHAT DOES HE LOOK LIKE?
BIG. BIG AND COVERED WITH BROWN FUR.
FRIEND OF MINE, ANOTHER MUSHER, WAS OUT IN A BLIZZARD ONE DAY. RAN SMACK INTO THE SNOW MONSTER. IT PICKED UP ONE OF THE DOGS. NEVER FOUND HIM. PITIFUL HOWLS.
HE'S PROBABLY A CARNIVORE, A MEAT-EATER. MOST ANIMALS AROUND HERE ARE.
I WANT TO HEAR ABOUT THE SNOWMAN--NOT YOUR STUPID FACTS!
CLICK
MY FRIEND AND ANOTHER GUY WENT OUT TO TRY TO CAPTURE THE SNOW MONSTER.

THEY NEVER CAME BACK.
SHE WAS LOOKING THROUGH HER TELESCOPE AND SPIED HIM OUT IN THE TUNDRA. HE WAS CHEWING ON BONES, SHE SAID. DON'T BELIEVE ME, GO ASK HER YOURSELF.
THEN MRS. CARTER OVER ON MAIN STREET SAW THE SNOW MONSTER A FEW DAYS LATER.
I'VE HEARD STORIES LIKE THIS BEFORE. SO FAR THEY HAVE NEVER TURNED OUT TO BE TRUE. I HAVE A FEELING THE ABOMINABLE SNOWMAN WILL BE NO DIFFERENT.
THAT MONSTER IS REAL--AND HE'S A *KILLER!*
IF WE GET INTO TROUBLE, I CAN RADIO THE RANGE STATION IN TOWN. THEY'LL SEND A HELICOPTER TO RESCUE US.
WAS AN ABOMINABLE SNOWMAN WAITING FOR US SOMEWHERE OUT THERE?

ARTHUR HAD BROUGHT ALONG FOUR ALASKA HUSKIES....
DAD SNAPPED PICTURES OF THE DOGS, US, ARTHUR AND THE SNOW.
CLICK
LOOK-- AN ANGEL!
COOL!
SPOOF
HEY! I'M GOING TO GET YOU FOR THAT!
BE CAREFUL, KIDS! STAY OUT OF TROUBLE!
WHAT KIND OF TROUBLE COULD WE GET INTO? THERE'S NOTHING BUT SNOW FOR MILES AROUND.
TRY AND CATCH ME, MISS FACTOID!
NAME-CALLING IS SO IMMATURE!
LUIS! LOOK OUT!
HEY--I'M NOT FALLING FOR THAT OLD TRI--
WHUUUZ?!
LUIS!

LUIS! ARE YOU ALL RIGHT?
GET ME OUT OF HERE!
DON'T WORRY, DAD'S COMING!
I LAY ON THE SNOW, TRYING TO CATCH MY BREATH.
IT WAS A MISTAKE TO HAUL KIDS ALONG.
WE STARTED WALKING AGAIN ACROSS THE SNOW.
SEE THAT SNOW RISE, ABOUT TEN MILES OFF? THAT'S WHERE THE MONSTER WAS LAST SPOTED.
WHERE WAS HE NOW? WAS HE HIDING SOMEWHERE, WATCHING US?
THAT'S THE ABANDONED MUSHER'S CABIN WHERE WE'LL STOP FOR THE NIGHT.
I CAN'T WAIT! IT MUST BE 2,000° OUT HERE!
MUSHERS DON'T STOP HERE ANYMORE BECAUSE THEY'RE AFRAID OF THE MONSTER.
AFTER SUPPER WE CRAWLED INTO OUR SLEEPING BAGS. I LAY AWAKE FOR A LONG TIME.
LISTENING FOR THE THUDDING FOOTSTEPS OF AN ABOMINABLE SNOWMAN.

MORNING!
I'M GOING TO CHECK ON THE DOGS. ARTHUR WENT OUT TO FEED THEM A FEW MINUTES AGO.
IT WAS COLD. THE FIRE ON THE STOVE HAD GONE OUT DURING THE NIGHT.
OH, WOW!
THIS IS INCREDIBLE!
HUGE FOOTPRINTS.
ENORMOUS FOOTPRINTS.
HE WAS HERE!
HOLD ON A MINUTE, LET'S NOT JUMP TO CONCLUSIONS....
WE HAVE TO GET AWAY FROM HERE--NOW!
HE'LL RIP US ALL TO SHREDS!
HEE HEE HEE
DO YOU THINK THEY'RE REAL?

YOU MEAN THE KID MADE THESE PRINTS? IT'S A JOKE?
LUIS, I SHOULD'VE KNOWN.
I'M AFRAID SO, ARTHUR.
I'VE GOT WORK TO DO.
WHILE YOU WERE ALL SLEEPING, I CARVED THE FOOTPRINTS OVER MY OWN PRINTS WITH MY MITTENS. THEN I STEPPED IN THE PRINTS ON MY WAY BACK, TO COVER MY TRACKS.
WE'RE NOT AT HOME IN PASADENA NOW. WE'RE OUT IN THE MIDDLE OF NOWHERE. THINGS COULD GET VERY DANGEROUS. YOU SAW THAT YESTERDAY WHEN YOU FELL DOWN THE CREVASSE.
NO MORE PRACTICAL JOKES. I'M HERE TO WORK. AND I DON'T WANT ANYTHING TO HAPPEN TO YOU, OR ANA, OR ANY OF US. UNDERSTOOD?
YES, DAD.
YOU THINK YOU'RE FUNNY BUT WAIT TILL YOU SEE THE SNOWMAN. WILL YOU BE LAUGHING THEN?

WE REACHED A STAND OF PINE TREES AT THE BASE OF THE SNOW RISE.
SUDDENLY, THE DOGS STOPPED SHORT. THEY REFUSED TO GO FARTHER.
MUSH!
CLICK
CLICK
WHAT'S WRONG WITH THEM?
ARTHUR'S RIGHT. SOMETHING DEFINITELY IS FRIGHTENING THE DOGS. THERE COULD BE A BEAR OR SOMETHING NEARBY.
NOT A BEAR, MR. GARCIA. THESE DOGS ARE SPOOKED, AND SO AM I.

NOT MUCH SCARES THESE DOGS. WHATEVER IT IS, IT'S SCARING THEM.
HOWLLL
HOWLLL
WE TRUDGED BACK TO THE CABIN.
ANA, WHY DON'T YOU AND LUIS GO GATHER UP SOME FIREWOOD. BUT BE CAREFUL!

LUIS! PUT YOUR KNAPSACK BACK ON! I DON'T WANT YOU GOING ANYWHERE WITHOUT IT! UNDERSTOOD?
WE'RE JUST GOING FOR FIREWOOD...I'M TIRED OF CARRYING IT.
NO ARGUMENTS. IF YOU GET LOST, THAT FOOD COULD KEEP YOU ALIVE UNTIL WE FIND YOU.
ANA AND I CRUNCHED ACROSS THE SNOW TO THE NEAREST TREES.
ANA--LOOK!
DON'T STEP ON IT, LUIS! YOU MIGHT FALL IN.
I WONDER IF THERE ARE FISH SWIMMING UNDER THERE.
TAP TAP
WE SHOULD TELL DAD ABOUT THIS. HE MIGHT WANT TO PHOTOGRAPH IT.
ANA TOLD DAD ABOUT THE FROZEN STREAM.
INTERESTING. I'LL GO TAKE A LOOK AT IT AFTER SUPPER. I'VE GOT TO FIND SOMETHING TO PHOTOGRAPH BESIDES ALL THIS ICE AND SNOW.
LET'S GO OUTSIDE AND BUILD A SNOWMAN OR SOMETHING.
CLICK
WE STEPPED OUTSIDE INTO THE COLD.
LISTEN!

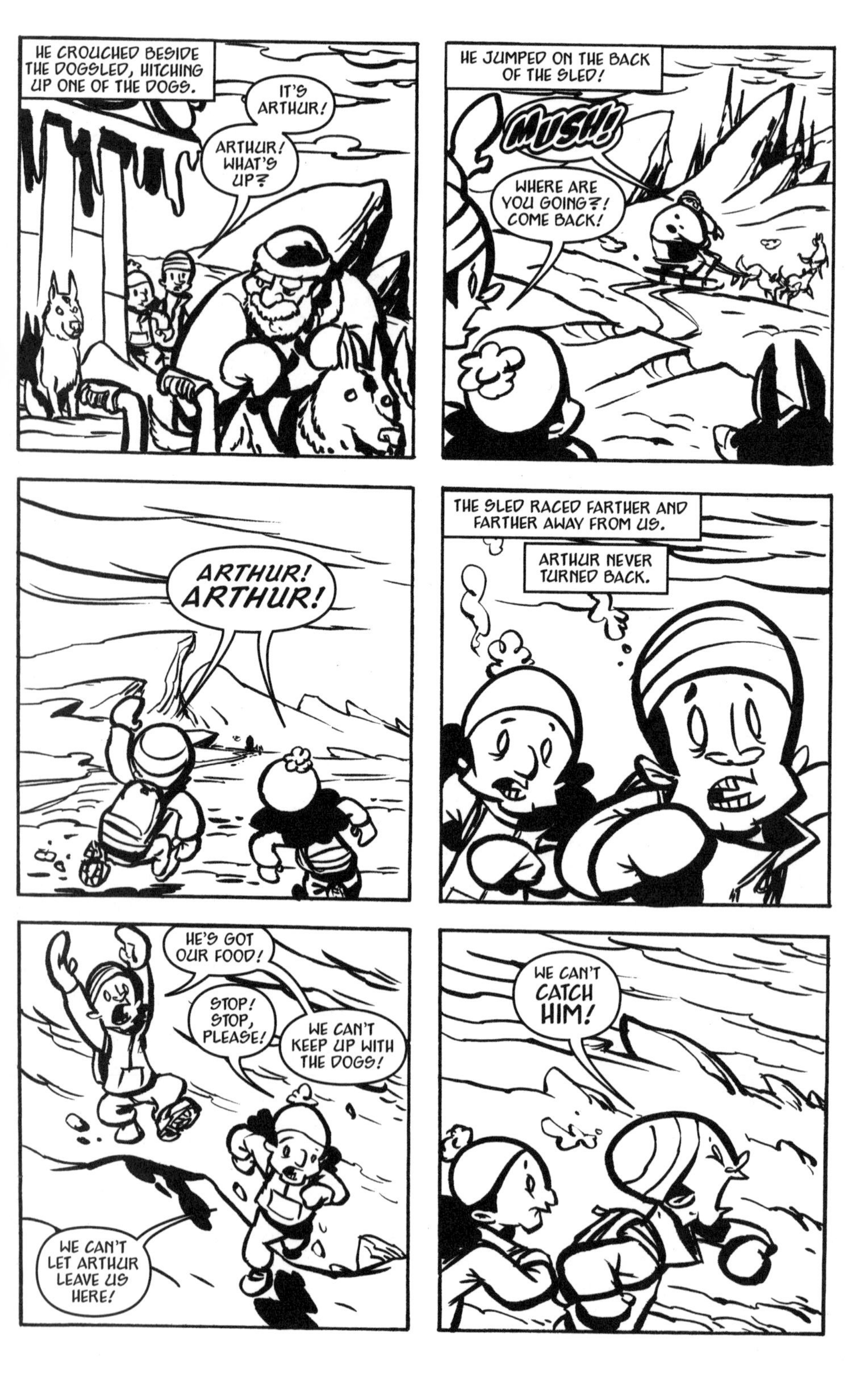
HE CROUCHED BESIDE THE DOGSLED, HITCHING UP ONE OF THE DOGS.
IT'S ARTHUR!
ARTHUR! WHAT'S UP?!
HE JUMPED ON THE BACK OF THE SLED!
MUSH!
WHERE ARE YOU GOING?! COME BACK!
ARTHUR! ARTHUR!
THE SLED RACED FARTHER AND FARTHER AWAY FROM US.
ARTHUR NEVER TURNED BACK.
HE'S GOT OUR FOOD!
STOP! STOP, PLEASE!
WE CAN'T KEEP UP WITH THE DOGS!
WE CAN'T LET ARTHUR LEAVE US HERE!
WE CAN'T CATCH HIM!

ALL AROUND US, NOTHING BUT SNOW. NO LANDMARKS. NO SIGN OF THE CABIN.
WHERE ARE WE?
THE CABIN IS THAT WAY! LET'S GO!
NO! THE CABIN'S THE OTHER WAY!
WE FOLLOWED OUR FOOTPRINTS FOR A SHORT WHILE.
IT WAS HARD TO SEE IN THE FALLING SNOW.
I CAN HARDLY SEE YOU!
LUIS, I'M GETTING SCARED!
DON'T WORRY. I BET DAD'S LOOKING FOR US RIGHT NOW!
DAD! DAD!
I THINK I SEE SOMETHING! COME ON!
SUDDENLY. I FELT MYSELF BEING SUCKED DOWN UNDER THE SNOW!

THE SNOW RUSHED UP, SWIRLED AROUND US... AND *BURIED* US.
WE'RE TRAPPED DOWN HERE! DAD WILL NEVER FIND US! NEVER!
DAAAD!!!
DAAAAADDDD!!!
DADAAAAAAAD!!
I CLAPPED A MITTEN OVER HER MOUTH.
TOO LATE.
CLAPP
I HEARD A LOW RUMBLING.
THE SNOW WALLS BEGAN TO CRACK AND CRUMBLE.
ANA HAD STARTED AN *AVALANCHE!*

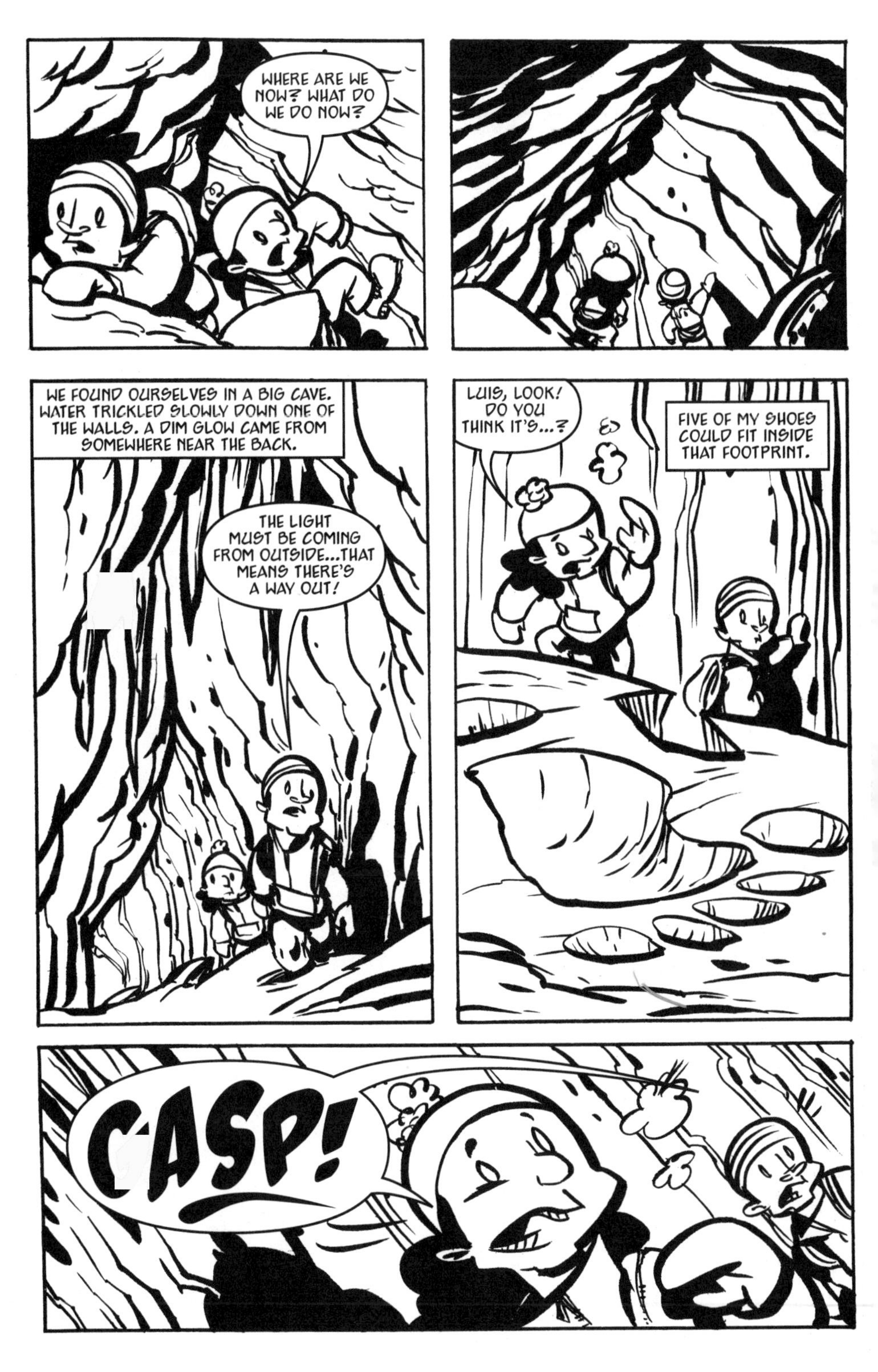
WHERE ARE WE NOW? WHAT DO WE DO NOW?
WE FOUND OURSELVES IN A BIG CAVE. WATER TRICKLED SLOWLY DOWN ONE OF THE WALLS. A DIM GLOW CAME FROM SOMEWHERE NEAR THE BACK.
THE LIGHT MUST BE COMING FROM OUTSIDE...THAT MEANS THERE'S A WAY OUT!
LUIS, LOOK! DO YOU THINK IT'S...?
FIVE OF MY SHOES COULD FIT INSIDE THAT FOOTPRINT.
ASP!

WE'RE TRAPPED!

HE'S FROZEN...
HUH?
MAYBE HE GOES INTO THE ICE TO REST, LIKE DRACULA IN HIS COFFIN.
LOOK AT HIS HANDS! OR PAWS, OR WHATEVER...
HE'S DEFINITELY A MAMMAL. THE FUR IS A DEAD GIVEAWAY.
THIS IS NO TIME FOR BIOLOGY LESSONS! WAIT UNTIL DAD SEES THIS. HE'LL GO CRAZY! IF HE CAN GET A PICTURE OF THIS, HE'LL BE FAMOUS!
YEAH, IF WE CAN FIND DAD. IF WE EVER GET OUT OF HERE.
AHA! I FOUND SOMETHING!
MAYBE THERE'S A SECRET DOOR HERE. A HIDDEN PASSAGE OR SOMETHING.
THAT'S JUST A CRACK.
KRRRRRAAAAKK
ALL YOU FOUND WAS A CRACK IN THE WALL.
THE ICE IS CRACKING! THE MONSTER... HE'S BREAKING OUT!
KRRAACCK

RUN!
WAIT! IT'S BLOCKED. THE AVALANCHE, REMEMBER?
MAYBE HE DIDN'T SEE US.
THEN WHY IS HE ROARING?
SNIFF
BOOM
HE'S CRUSHING ME!
LET GO OF HER!

RIPP
HEY!
TRAIL MIX
SNIFF
WEIRD! HE LIKES TRAIL MIX.
THAT'S ALL THERE IS....
RAWWRR
GRAB
GRAB

PLEASE DON'T EAT US!
WHERE'S HE TAKING US?
MAYBE HE WANTS TO ROAST US. MAYBE HE DOESN'T LIKE KIDS RAW.
WHY DIDN'T WE SEE THAT BEFORE? MAYBE WE COULD HAVE ESCAPED!
TOO LATE NOW...
POOR DAD. HE'LL NEVER KNOW WHAT HAPPENED TO US.
UNLESS HE FINDS OUR BONES IN THE SNOW.
SNIFF
SNIFF
BARK
BARK
BARK

DROP!
DROP!
BARK
BARK
BARK
IS HE CHASING US?
KEEP RUNNING!
THE CABIN!
BARK
BARK
BARK
DAD! DAD! WE FOUND HIM! WE FOUND THE ABOMINABLE SNOWMAN!
THE CABIN STOOD EMPTY. EMPTY AND BARE. DAD WAS GONE.
DAD?
WE--WE'RE ALL ALONE.

AT LEAST THE SNOWMAN DIDN'T FOLLOW US.
LUIS... WHY DID HE DROP US?
I THINK THE BARKING DOG SCARED HIM.

THE SNOWMAN! HE'S BACK! HIDE!!!
BARK
BARK

LUIS? ANA?

DAD!
WHAT'S GOING ON, GUYS?
WHERE'S ARTHUR?

HE TOOK OFF! HE TOOK THE SLED! HE TOOK ALL THE FOOD AND THREE OF THE DOGS!

I'D BETTER RADIO FOR HELP. WE WON'T LAST LONG WITHOUT FOOD.

DAD--LISTEN! ANA AND I FOUND THE ABOMINABLE SNOWMAN!
THIS IS NO TIME FOR JOKES, LUIS. IF WE DON'T GET HELP, WE COULD STARVE TO DEATH OUT HERE!

HE'S NOT JOKING, DAD.

WE LED HIM OUT TO THE SNOW.

WHY SHOULD I BELIEVE THIS? YOU FAKED THE SNOWMAN'S FOOTPRINTS THIS MORNING, LUIS. THESE JUST LOOK A LITTLE BIGGER.
WE'LL SHOW YOU THE CAVE, DAD! FOLLOW THE FOOTPRINTS. YOU'LL SEE. IT'S UNBELIEVABLE.

THE CAVE IS DOWN THAT HOLE.

LET'S GO CHECK IT OUT!
DAD...WAIT! YOU DON'T UNDERSTAND. THERE'S A MONSTER DOWN THERE!
I WANT TO SEE THIS FOR MYSELF.

I HAD A BAD FEELING.
A VERY BAD FEELING.
CLICK
THIS IS AMAZING!
INCREDIBLE!
HOW DOES HE DO THAT?

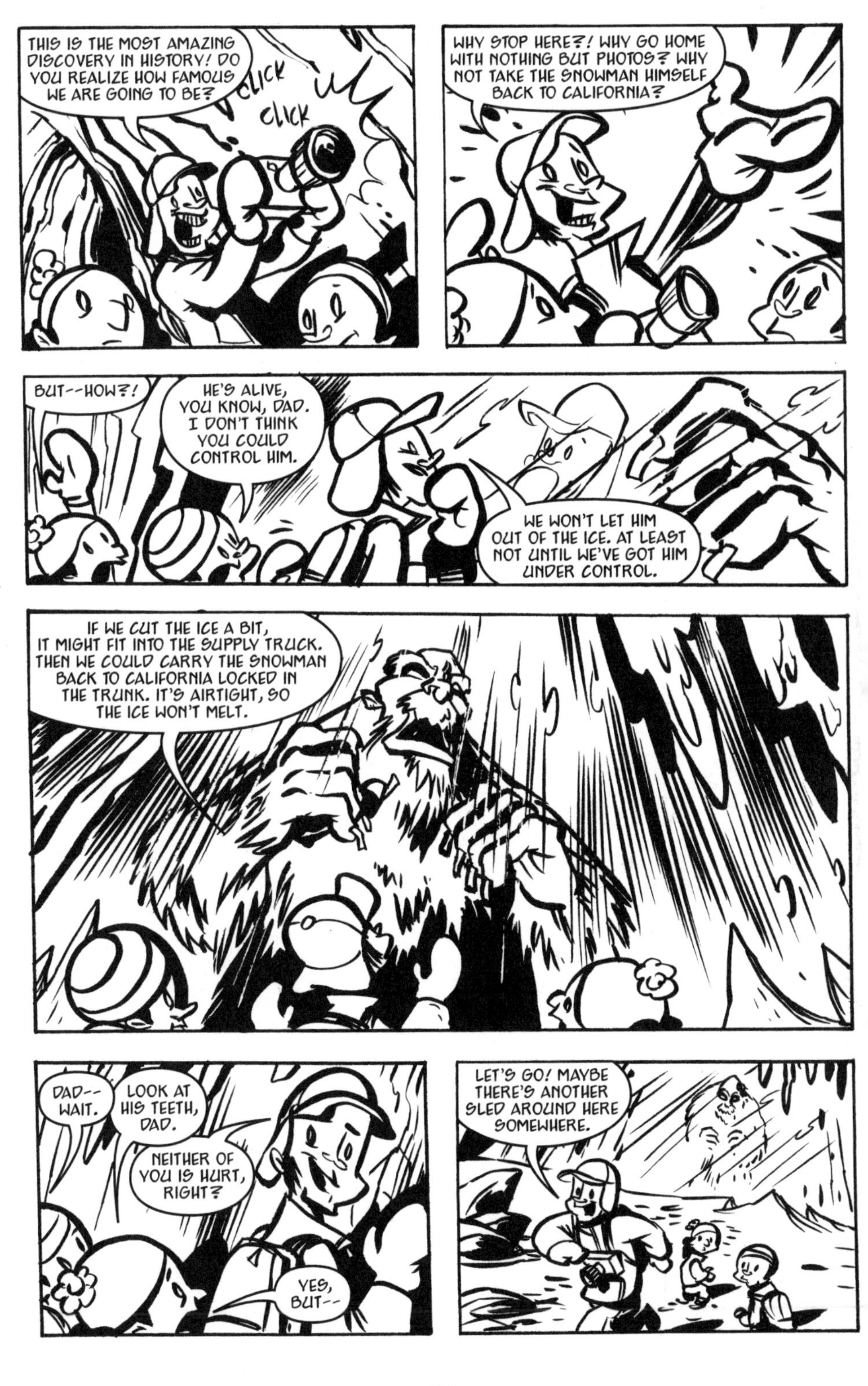
THIS IS THE MOST AMAZING DISCOVERY IN HISTORY! DO YOU REALIZE HOW FAMOUS WE ARE GOING TO BE?
CLICK
CLICK
WHY STOP HERE?! WHY GO HOME WITH NOTHING BUT PHOTOS? WHY NOT TAKE THE SNOWMAN HIMSELF BACK TO CALIFORNIA?
BUT--HOW?!
HE'S ALIVE, YOU KNOW, DAD. I DON'T THINK YOU COULD CONTROL HIM.
WE WON'T LET HIM OUT OF THE ICE. AT LEAST NOT UNTIL WE'VE GOT HIM UNDER CONTROL.
IF WE CUT THE ICE A BIT, IT MIGHT FIT INTO THE SUPPLY TRUCK. THEN WE COULD CARRY THE SNOWMAN BACK TO CALIFORNIA LOCKED IN THE TRUNK. IT'S AIRTIGHT, SO THE ICE WON'T MELT.
DAD-- WAIT.
LOOK AT HIS TEETH, DAD.
NEITHER OF YOU IS HURT, RIGHT?
YES, BUT--
LET'S GO! MAYBE THERE'S ANOTHER SLED AROUND HERE SOMEWHERE.

WE HITCHED UP OUR ONLY DOG AND TOWED THE SUPPLY TRUNK TO THE CAVE.
DAD BEGAN TO CUT THE ICE DOWN TO SIZE WITH A HACKSAW.
CRACKK
LOOK OUT! HE'S BREAKING OUT!
I CRACKED THE ICE A BIT, LUIS.

I OPENED THE LID OF THE TRUNK.
IT JUST BARELY FIT.
LET'S SNEAK SOME SNOWBALLS INTO THE TRUNK.
THEY WON'T MELT IN THERE. WE CAN THROW THEM WHEN WE GET HOME.
READY? ONE, TWO, THREE, HEAVE!
SEE, LUIS? NOTHING TERRIBLE HAPPENED.
WE'RE LUCKY!
I'M GOING TO RADIO FOR HELP.
WE'RE GOING HOME! HOME TO SUNNY, HOT PASADENA!
I'M GOING TO KISS A PALM TREE! I NEVER WANT TO SEE SNOW AGAIN!
I HAD NO IDEA THAT OUR SNOW ADVENTURE WAS JUST BEGINNING.

THE COLD, THE WIND BLOWING OVER THE ROLLING WHITE TUNDRA. THE SNARLING ABOMINABLE SNOWMAN. IT ALL SEEMED LIKE A DREAM.
BUT I KNEW IT WAS NO DREAM.
THE RADIO SAID IT'S A HUNDRED DEGREES TODAY!
I LOVE IT! LOVE IT!
LAUREN CAME OVER TO HEAR ABOUT OUR TRIP. I WANTED TO TELL HER THE WHOLE STORY, BUT DAD TOLD US TO KEEP QUIET ABOUT IT.
I DON'T BELEIVE YOU TWO! A WEEK AGO YOU COULDN'T SHUT UP ABOUT SNOW. NOW YOU'RE LETTING THE SUN BURN YOU TO A CRISP!
TELL ME ABOUT THE TRIP!
TAN
IT'S A SECRET.
A SECRET? WHAT KIND OF SECRET?
I'M GOING INTO THE CITY NOW.
DAD HAD A MEETING WITH SOME SCIENTISTS.
HE WANTED TO TURN THE ABOMINABLE SNOWMAN OVER TO THE RIGHT PEOPLE, TO BE SURE THE SNOWMAN WOULD BE TREATED WELL.
LUIS AND ANA, ARE YOU LISTENING? DON'T TOUCH THE SUPPLY TRUNK. STAY AWAY FROM IT--
GOTCHA, DAD.

WHAT'S IN THE SUPPLY TRUNK?
C'MON, SPILL! I WON'T LEAVE YOU ALONE UNTIL YOU TELL ME!
WE FOUND HIM! WE FOUND HIM AND WE BROUGHT HIM BACK!
FOUND WHO?
THE ABOMINABLE SNOWMAN!
SURE. AND DID YOU FIND THE TOOTH FAIRY UP THERE, TOO?
PROVE IT. YOU'RE MAKING IT ALL UP. YOU THINK YOU'RE REALLY FUNNY.
Hee Hee Hee Hee Hee

COME ON, WE WON'T HURT ANYTHING. WE'LL JUST PULL OPEN THE LID A TINY BIT SO LAUREN CAN SEE HIM.
WE BETTER NOT.
OH, COME ON. THERE'S NO ABOMINABLE SNOWMAN. YOU TWO ARE RIDICULOUS.
WE'RE NOT RIDICULOUS!
WE MIGHT AS WELL SHOW HER.
AAAIIIIGGGHHHH!!!!!
GOTCHA!
LUIS! YOU CREEP!
NOOGIE NOOGIE
AAAAIIIIGGGGHHHH!!!!
IT'S OKAY, LAUREN! HE CAN'T HURT YOU! HE'S FROZEN!

NOW YOU BELIEVE US?
IT'S... AWESOME!
THAT CREATURE IS JUST SO AWESOME! WHAT IS YOUR DAD GOING TO DO WITH HIM?
WE'RE NOT SURE YET. DAD'S TRYING TO FIGURE THAT OUT.
HEY, LAUREN! THINK FAST!
FLING
SPLAT!
NICE SHOT, ACE.
WHU..?

WOW! ANA... HOW DID YOU DO THAT?
LUIS...THIS ISN'T RIGHT. WE SHOULD HAVE LEFT THIS SNOW IN THE CAVE. IT ISN'T NORMAL SNOW.
THIS IS TOO WEIRD! IT'S A HUNDRED DEGREES OUT, AND THE SNOW ISN'T MELTING!
SNOW! SNOW! IT'S WONDERFUL! SNOW IN PASADENA!
SNOWBALL FIGHT!
FLING!
POOMF
ANA... ARE YOU OKAY?
CAN YOU HEAR ME? ANA?

IF WE GET HER IN THE WARM HOUSE, MAYBE WE CAN WARM HER UP!
WE STOOD ANA IN FRONT OF THE OVEN.
SHE'S SO FREEZING! HOW CAN WE MELT THE SNOW?
CLICK
OVEN
IT'S NOT WORKING. NOTHING'S HAPPENING!
WE HAVE TO TRY SOMETHING ELSE...SOMETHING ELSE...
THE FURNACE! WE'LL HOLD HER IN FRONT OF THE FURNACE!
THE ICE DIDN'T MELT! MY SISTER REMAINED A HUMAN SNOW CONE!
I SUDDENLY REMEMBERED HOW WARM THE ABOMINABLE SNOWMAN FELT WHEN HE CARRIED US ACROSS THE ALASKAN TUNDRA; HEAT POURED OFF THE CREATURE'S BODY.
COME ON, LAUREN!
TRAIL MIX
TRAIL MIX? LUIS, CAN'T YOU WAIT TO EAT LATER?
IT'S NOT FOR ME--IT'S FOR HIM!
TRAIL MIX

CREAKk
COME ON, YOU KNOW YOU LOVE TRAIL MIX! WAKE UP!
PLOP!
TRAIL MIX
craaakkk
TRAIL MIX
TRAIL MIX™
CRRaaakkk

CRAAACK
AAAIIGGHH!
IT'S ALIVE!
SNATCH!
TRAIL MIX
SHAKE
SHAKE
TRAIL MIX
MUNCH
MUNCH
MAKE HIM GO BACK INTO THE TRUNK!
ARE YOU CRAZY? HOW CAN I DO THAT?
CHEW
CHEW
CHEW
TRAIL MIX
SNIFF
SNIFF
SNIFF

HUG
LUIS... LOOK!
IT'S WORKING! HE'S DEFROSTING HER!
DRIP
DRIP
DRIP
THANK YOU!

HE'S ESCAPING!
RWAAAWWRRR!
BUT THE BIG, FURRY CREATURE HAD MORE SURPRISES IN STORE.
RWAAAWWRRK!
WITH A LOUD GRUNT, THE SNOW APPEARED TO STICK TO HIS FUR!

BOOM
BOOM
BOOM
BEFORE LONG, THE LAST OF THE SNOW HAD VANISHED....
WAIT! COME BACK!
AT LEAST DAD HAS HIS PHOTOS....
GULP
HEY, KIDS, I'M HOME! HOW'S OUR SNOWMAN DOING?
VRROOOMmm....

WE ATE SUPPER EARLY THAT EVENING. THINGS WERE PRETTY QUIET AROUND THE DINNER TABLE.
I'M GLAD YOU KIDS ARE SAFE AND SOUND. THAT'S WHAT COUNTS.
I'LL TELL THE MUSEUM OF NATURAL HISTORY THAT THEY'LL HAVE TO MAKE DO WITH THE PHOTOGRAPHS.
PHOTOGRAPHS ARE BETTER THAN NOTHING.
ARE YOU CRAZY?! THOSE PICTURES ARE GOING TO AMAZE THE WHOLE WORLD!
WE SAT QUIETLY UNDER THE RED LIGHT WHILE DAD DEVELOPED THE NEGATIVES.
HUH?
I DON'T REMEMBER TAKING THOSE SHOTS...
I'M NOT PLAYING ANY TRICKS! I SWEAR!
THE ABOMINABLE SNOWMAN--HE SHOULD BE STANDING RIGHT THERE!
THE TUNDRA SHOT CAME OUT FINE--THE DOGS, THE SLED, THE ELK HERD--BUT THE SHOTS IN THE MONSTER'S CAVE--?!
I DON'T GET IT! NOT A SINGLE SHOT OF THE CREATURE! NOT ONE!
NO ABOMINABLE SNOWMAN.
IT WAS ALMOST AS IF HE NEVER EXISTED. AS IF THE WHOLE THING NEVER HAPPENED.

PASADENA AVE.
RRRAAAAWWWRRRRR!!!!!

MEET THE ARTIST

Gabriel Hernandez

Gabriel Hernandez studied fine arts in Granada, Spain, where he now lives with his wife, Violeta, and his daughters, Clara and Lucia. He has illustrated several childrens' books and exhibited his paintings. Gabriel has created comic art for IDW comics; *CVO: Artifact;* and *CVO: Human Touch,* among others. He also is the artist for Clive Barker's The Thief of Always graphic novel series.

Gabriel sketched and summarized the text for *The Werewolf of Fever Swamp*. Then he created a rough storyboard without text (**A**), followed by one with text. Then he did a definitive storyboard. (**B**) He drew sketches of key characters, including expressions, movements, as well as some scenery. (**C**) Finally, Gabriel drew all the page sketches, inked over his sketches, filled in the details, added watercolors, and did all the speech bubbles and lettering by hand so it became part of the artwork.

MEET THE ARTIST

Greg Ruth

Born in Texas, Greg Ruth began working in comics in 1993 with *Sudden Gravity* and has produced work for The Factoid Books, The Duplex Planet, The Matrix Comics, *Freaks of the Heartland*, and *Conan*. He has also done illustrations for *The New York Times*, worked on murals for Grand Central Terminal, and contributed to two music videos for Prince and Rob Thomas.Greg recently illustrated a new Scholastic series, *Sherlock Holmes and The Baker Street Irregulars*, and is currently at work on his own original graphic novel for Graphix, a spooky, suspenseful story of a child who disappeared, the tape of clues he left behind, and the boy who sets off into an unearthly forest world to solve the mystery.

Greg doesn't do sketches. He boldly jumps in and draws the art all at once.

Greg read through the original book of *The Scarecrow Walks at Midnight*, scribbled notes, and crossed out blocks of text or whole chapters with page counts. He then created a group of drawings to go with the scenes he had left, basically figuring out what each page contained and how it would break out into panels. Greg drew by hand, first doing the big parts of the page, its "beats," and then filling in the rest. He electronically scanned the artwork into his computer so he could assemble the pages and create the speech balloons and lettering. Finally, he went to bed each night, just as the sun was coming up, for a few hours of nightmares and then woke up — to repeat the process again and again and again!

MEET THE ARTIST

Scott Morse

Scott Morse is the award-winning author of more than ten graphic novels, including *Soulwind; The Barefoot Serpent;* and *Southpaw*. He is also the creator of the *Magic Pickle*, a hilarious story about a dilly of a superhero who's fighting against evil vegetables trying to take over the world. Scott is working on two illustrated *Magic Pickle* chapter books and a graphic novel for Scholastic. He lives with his family in Oakland, California, where he works as a storyteller in both animation and comics.

Scott's character sketches

Scott first adapted *The Abominable Snowman of Pasadena* into a script that broke down the story into pages and panels. He drew sketches, based on this script, and then penciled and inked the final art. This original art was scanned and sent as an electronic file to a professional letterer who added the speech bubbles, dialogue, and captions to the pages by computer.

TALES TO COME!

SCARY SUMMER

Wish that summer would never end? Not *THIS* summer!

Someone's creeping through the garden, whispering nasty things, smashing melons and squashing tomatoes, but those funky lawn ornaments can't move . . . *right?* **Dean Haspiel**, a veteran of Batman and Justice League comics and the acclaimed artist on *The Quitter*, knows just how to portray the ***Revenge of The Lawn Gnomes***.

In his award-winning comic series like The Bakers and Plastic Man, **Kyle Baker** proves he's one funny artist. The perfect guy to draw a story about a summer camp where it's all fun and games and everybody's happy. Too happy . . . That's why one young girl is out to uncover ***The Horror at Camp Jellyjam***.

Sandy beaches, tidal pools, shoreline caves . . . *ghosts!* A brother and sister's seaside vacation turns spooky at ***Ghost Beach*** by **Ted Naifeh**, Gothic master and creator of the creepy Courtney Crumrin series; the upcoming Polly and the Pirates series; and Unearthly, a sci-fi comedy manga series.

AVAILABLE IN JULY 2007

THE POWERS OF POPULARITY CAN STING!

Get ready for middle-school mischief and superpower mayhem in this hilarious new series about two psychokinetic girls locked in a heated popularity competition.

AND COMING SOON...

QUEEN BEE #2